PEARSON LANGUAGE CENTRAL

ELD

Consulting Authors

Jim Cummins, Ph.D.

Lily Wong Fillmore, Ph.D.

Georgia García, Ph.D.

Jill Kerper Mora, Ed.D.

Glenview, Illinois • Boston, Massachusetts • Chandler, Arizona •
Upper Saddle River, New Jersey

ISBN-13:   978-0-328-63433-0
ISBN-10:   0-328-63433-6
10 11 12 13 V011 18 17 16 15 14

Get Online!

Readiness Unit
Homes and Families

Get Online!

Hear it!
See it!
Do it!

- Big Idea Video
- Concept Talk Video
- Envision It! Animation
- Grammar Jammer

Homes and Families

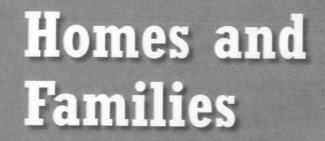

THE BIG ? What is all around me?

Readiness Unit

Around Home
What is around us at home?

Our Family
Who is in our family?

Outside Our Door
What is outside our door?

Neighborhood Friends
What can we do with our neighborhood friends?

Around School
What is around us at school?

Around the Neighborhood
What can we see around our neighborhood?

bedroom

PICTURE IT!

green

home

favorite
moved
see

What is around us at home?

There are many things around us at home. Home is where you keep your clothes and toys.

Read the passage together.
Then circle the vocabulary words.

Jenny's Home

Jenny (moved) into her new home.

She was happy to see her new bedroom.

Her mom had painted the bedroom green.

Green was her favorite color!

Jenny liked her new bedroom.

Talk About It Complete the
sentences below.

Jenny moved _____.
into her new home, into a new bedroom

Jenny liked _____.
green, her new bedroom

Your Turn Why was Jenny happy?
Tell a partner.

Describing We use words to tell about people we know or people in stories. Special words help us describe people.

Some words tell how people feel.
Some words tell what people are like.

Yun is **sad.**   Mark is **happy.**   Ty is **helpful.**

Talk About It Say a sentence that tells about you.

I am _____.

Your Turn Look at the girl in the picture. Write a sentence that tells about the girl.

The girl is _____.

Character The people and animals in stories are called **characters.**

Molly likes to make dinner with her mom. Her brother Mike helps too. He likes to make bread.

· ·

Talk About It Describe the characters in the story above. What do they like to do?

> Molly is _____. She likes to _____.
>
> Mike is _____. He likes to _____.

· ·

Your Turn Read the story on page R7. Then draw a picture of how Jenny feels at the end of the story.

Nouns The names of people and things are **nouns.** When there is more than one thing or person, we often add -s to the end of the word.

Circle the pictures that show more than one thing or person.

Things	bed	bed(s)	
	toy	toy(s)	
People	girl	girl(s)	
	boy	boy(s)	

Talk About It Say the name of a thing in your home. Say the name of a person in your home.

Your Turn Add a letter to make the nouns more than one.

toy____   sister____   bed____

Around Home Think about all of the things that are around you at home. What do you see in the picture?

Talk About It Look at the words on page R6. Tell about each word.

Produce Language Fill in the web below. Then write a sentence or draw a picture in your Weekly Concept Journal.

Home

Vocabulary

baby

grandma

grandpa

care
like
together

Who is in our family?

Families can have moms, dads, and grandparents. Sometimes a new baby brother or sister becomes part of a family too.

Read the passage together.
Then circle the vocabulary words.

Cathy's Family

Cathy takes (care) of her baby sister.

Her family takes care of the baby too.

Their grandma and grandpa come to visit.

They like to hold the baby and feed her.

Cathy has fun when her family is together.

Talk About It Complete the
sentences below.

Cathy has _____ in her family.
a baby sister, a grandma, a grandpa

Cathy likes _____.
to take care of her sister, her family

Your Turn Who is in your family?
Tell a partner.

R13

Describing We use words to tell about places we know or places in stories.

Some words tell about the size of a place. Some words tell what the place looks like.

The family had a **big** yard.

The kitchen was **small.**

It was **dark** outside.

Talk About It Say a sentence that tells about the size of the place you are in now.

The room is _____ .

Your Turn Write a sentence that tells about the size or color of your favorite place.

My favorite place is _____ .

Setting Stories happen at different times and places. Look for clues to tell when and where the story happens.

Cathy finished dinner.
She heard the baby crying.
She walked into the baby's room.

- -

Talk About It Where does the story happen?

The story happens in a _____ .

- -

Your Turn Read the story on page R13. Circle the picture that shows where the story about Cathy happens.

Nouns One kind of **noun** names a place. When we tell about a noun that means more than one, we often add -s to the end of the word.

home

home(s)

building

building(s)

· ·

Talk About It What are the places in the sentences below? Circle the places.

We went to school. Then we went to the park.

· ·

Your Turn Add a letter to make the nouns more than one.

home____   room____   building____

Our Family Think about all of the people who are in a family. Who do you see in the picture?

Talk About It Look at the words on page R12. Tell about each word.

Produce Language Draw a picture below. Show a family. Then write or draw in your Weekly Concept Journal.

Vocabulary

PICTURE IT!

bird

PICTURE IT!

flowers

PICTURE IT!

yellow

fun
look
outside

What is outside our door?

You can see animals outside. You can see trees and flowers too.

Read the passage together.
Then circle the vocabulary words.

Fun Outside

Aunt Fay and I walked (outside).

We saw flowers. Some were yellow.

She saw a bird in the bird house.

She said, "Look! Do you see the bird?"

I said, "Yes, I see it!"

It was fun to be outside.

Talk About It Complete
the sentence below.

> You can see _____ outside.
> *birds, flowers*

Your Turn What have you
seen outside? Tell a partner.

Literary Analysis We use special words to talk about what happens in stories.

The **beginning** is the start of the story.

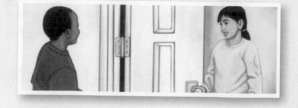

The **middle** is what happens next.

The **end** is what happens last.

Talk About It Tell what happens in the story.

In the _____, the girl's friend comes over.

In the _____, they play outside.

In the _____, the girl's friend leaves.

Your Turn Tell a story. Say what will happen in the beginning.

Plot A story's **plot** is what happens in the beginning, middle, and end of the story.

Frank went outside.

Frank picked a flower.

Frank gave the flower to his mom.

Talk About It What happens in the story?

In the beginning, _____.

In the middle, _____.

In the end, _____.

Your Turn Read the story on page R19.
Tell what happens at the end of the story.

Verbs Action words are called **verbs.**

walks

runs

jumps

eats

plays

sleeps

Talk About It What are the verbs in the sentences below? Circle the verbs.

Rosa walks in the rain.

Sam jumps in the water.

Your Turn Use a verb from above to complete the sentence.

Sally _____ outside.

Outside Our Door Think about all of the things that are outside. What do you see in the picture?

Talk About It Look at the words on page R18. Tell about each word.

Produce Language Fill in the web below. Then write a sentence or draw a picture in your Weekly Concept Journal.

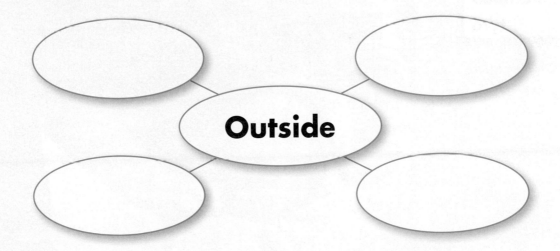

Outside

Vocabulary

PICTURE IT!

dog

PICTURE IT!

mail carrier

friendly

neighbor

neighborhood

two

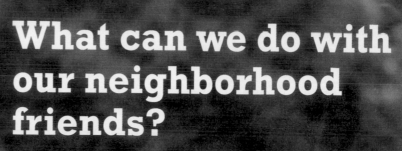

What can we do with our neighborhood friends?

Families and their pets live in the neighborhood. Friends and neighbors live there too.

Read the passage together.
Then circle the vocabulary words.

Around the Neighborhood

Dad and I walked our (dog) Rex today.

Our neighbor Ms. Dot said hello.

Then she gave Rex a treat.

Dan the mail carrier stopped to pet Rex.

We saw two friendly neighbors today!

· ·

Talk About It Complete the sentence below.

> They saw _____ in the neighborhood.
> *friendly neighbors, the mail carrier*

· ·

Your Turn How do you spend time with your neighbors? Tell a partner.

Literary Analysis We use words to tell about stories. We use the word *is* when we tell about a story.

The story is make-believe.

The story is funny.

· ·

Talk About It Look at the picture.
Tell about the story.

_____ about music.

_____ about neighbors.

· ·

Your Turn Think of your favorite story.
Tell about the story. Use the word *is*.

Realism and Fantasy Some stories are make-believe. Other stories could really happen.

Circle things in this picture that show this story is make-believe.

Circle things in this picture that show this story could really happen.

Talk About It How do you know the first story is make-believe? How do you know the second story could really happen? Tell a partner.

Your Turn Read the story on page R25. Is this story make-believe, or could it really happen?

Simple Sentences A **sentence** names someone or something. Then it tells what the person or the thing is or does.

A dog ran in the park.

capital   period

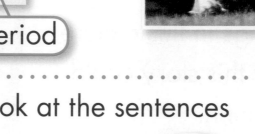

The bike is new.

capital   period

Talk About It Look at the sentences below. What is missing?

dana plays on a swing

tim rides a bike

Your Turn Write your own sentence. Tell something you do.

I _____ .

Neighborhood Friends

What can we do with our neighborhood friends? Think about all of the people in your neighborhood. What do you see in the picture?

Talk About It Look at the words on page R24. Tell about each word.

Produce Language Fill in the web below. Then write a sentence or draw a picture in your Weekly Concept Journal.

Neighborhood Friends

Vocabulary

backpack

classroom

teacher

he

read

What is around us at school?

At school teachers and friends help us learn. Books and cards also help us learn.

Read the passage together.
Then circle the vocabulary words.

First Grade

Rob felt scared on the first day of school.

(He) went to his first grade classroom.

He put his backpack on a hook.

Then his teacher read his favorite book!

He thought, "School is going to be fun."

Rob was happy about being in first grade.

. . . .

Talk About It Complete the
sentence below.

When Rob got to school, he _____.
felt scared, went to his classroom

. . . .

Your Turn Why did Rob think
school would be fun? Tell a partner.

Describing We use words to describe, or tell about, what is happening.

The girl **is reading.**

The children **are working.**

The children **are playing.**

Talk About It Say a sentence that tells what you and a friend could be doing.

We _____ .

Your Turn Look at the picture. Write a sentence that tells what is happening.

The children _____ .

Plot A story's **plot** is what happens in the beginning, middle, and end of the story.

Rob is going to school. → Rob is making a new friend. → Rob is going home.

Talk About It What happens in the story?

In the beginning, _____.

In the middle, _____.

In the end, _____.

Your Turn Read the story on page R31. Tell what happens in the beginning, middle, and end of the story.

Adjectives Words that describe people, places, or things are called **adjectives.** Adjectives can tell what kind or how many.

color	red crayon	green folder
number	two pencils	three erasers
size	big ball	small cat

Talk About It What are the adjectives in the sentences below? Circle the adjectives.

Maya gave me a yellow crayon.

There were three folders.

Your Turn Use an adjective from the chart to tell about the picture.

_____ pencils

R34

Around School Think about all of the things that are around you at school. What do you see in the picture?

- -

Talk About It Look at the words on page R30. Tell about each word.

- -

Produce Language Fill in the web below. Then write a sentence or draw a picture in your Weekly Concept Journal.

School

Vocabulary

fruit

vegetables

**buy
market
visit
where**

What can we see around our neighborhood?

There are many things in the neighborhood. Many neighborhoods have a market.

Read the passage together.
Then circle the vocabulary words.

To Market!

My mom and I (visit) the market.

That's where we buy fruit and vegetables.

People sell food and flowers too.

My mom also buys a treat for me.

I love to go there!

Talk About It Complete the sentence below.

At the market, you can buy _____.
fruits and vegetables, flowers, food

Your Turn Why does the girl like to go to the market with her mom? Tell a partner.

Expressing Needs and Likes We use words to talk about things that we like and don't like. When we talk about stories, we can say whether we like or don't like them too.

I like the library.

I like the market.

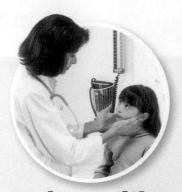

I don't like being sick.

Talk About It Look at the picture. Tell if you like or don't like these things.

I _____ apples.

I _____ bananas.

I _____ oranges.

Your Turn Tell something you like or don't like.

Realism and Fantasy A story can be make-believe, or it can be about something that could really happen. Read the story below.

Mama Bear, Papa Bear, and Baby Bear went to the market to buy honey.

Talk About It Is the story above make-believe, or could it really happen? Circle some clues in the picture above.

The story is _____.

I know because _____.

Your Turn Read the story on page R37. Is this story make-believe, or could it really happen? Did you like the story? Tell why.

Sentences A **sentence** has nouns and verbs. A sentence names someone or something and tells what the person or the thing is or does. The verbs are circled in the sentences below.

Sara (buys) food at the store.

Paul (wants) some vegetables.

The apples (are) red.

Talk About It
Circle the verbs in these two sentences.

> He sells fruit at the market.
>
> The vegetables are green.

Your Turn Write your own sentence. Tell about something you want from a market.

I _____ .

Around the Neighborhood

Think about all of the things that are around you in the neighborhood. What do you see in the picture?

Talk About It Look at the words on page R36. Tell about each word.

Produce Language Fill in the web below. Then write a sentence or draw a picture in your Weekly Concept Journal.

Neighborhood

baby

backpack

bedroom

bird

classroom

dog

flowers

fruit

grandma

grandpa

green

home

mail carrier

teacher

vegetables

yellow

Illustrations

R20 Rick Drennan; R27 Rick Drennan; R33 Sheenen Bersani; R39 Kathy McCord.

Photographs

Every effort has been made to secure permission and provide appropriate credit for photographic material. The publisher deeply regrets any omission and pledges to correct errors called to its attention in subsequent editions.

Unless otherwise acknowledged, all photographs are the property of Pearson Education, Inc.

Photo locators denoted as follows: Top (T), Center (C), Bottom (B), Left (L), Right (R), Background (Bkgd)

R6 (TL) ©Greg Wright/Alamy, (BL) ©Cydney Conger/Corbis, (C) Redcover.com/Getty Images; R8 (TL) Julia Fishkin/Jupiter Images, (TC) Ryan McVay/Getty Images, (CR) Jupiterimages/Jupiter Images, (BR) Diana Koenigsberg/Jupiter Images; R9 (TR) ©PhotoAlto/Alamy; R10 (TL) Andy Crawford and Gary Ombler/©DK Images, (CR) Steve Shott/©DK Images, (CL) ©Jupiterimages/BananaStock/Alamy, (CR) Lilly Dong/Jupiter Images; R11 (TC) Elizabeth Whiting & Associates/Corbis; R12 (TL) Jupiter Images, (CL) Getty Images, (C) Zia Solell/Getty Images, (BL) Lilly Dong/Jupiter Images; R14 (TL) Jupiter Images, (TC) Ken Hayden/Getty Images, (TR) ©Design Pics Inc./Alamy; R15 (TR) Getty Images, (BL) ©Corbis Premium RF/Alamy, (BR) ©Jupiterimages/Creatas/Alamy, (BC) ©Jupiterimages/Comstock Images/Alamy; R16 (TL) ©Jupiterimages/Creatas/Alamy, (CL) ©Glow Images/Alamy, (TC) ImageShop/Jupiter Images, (TR) ©Jupiterimages/Creatas/Alamy; R17 (TR) Megan Maloy/Getty Images; R18 (TL) ©Kfleen/Fotolia, (CL) Neil Fletcher/©DK Images; (C) Lillian Elaine Wilson/Jupiter Images; R19 (CR) Cyril Laubscher/©DK Images; R21 (TL) Getty Images, (TR) ©Jupiterimages/Polka Dot/Alamy, (TC) Ron Evans/Getty Images; R22 (TL) Jupiter Images, (TC) Getty Images, (TR) Nancy Brown/Getty Images, (CL) LWA/Getty Images, (CC) Sami Sarkis/Getty Images, (CR) DCA Productions/Getty Images, (BR) Getty Images; R23 (CR) BrandX Pictures/Jupiter Images; R24 (TL) Jupiter Images, (CL) ©Comstock Inc., (C) Pixtal/Punchstock; R26 (TL) Blue Lantern Studio/Corbis, (TR) ©Jupiterimages/Creatas/Alamy, (BR) ©Blend Images/Alamy; R27(CR) Ed Kashi/Corbis; R28(BR) Torahiko Yamashita, (TR) Bread and Butter/Getty Images; R29 Jupiter Images; R30(TL) Getty Images, (CL) Getty Images, (BL) Getty Images, (C) Jose Luis Pelaez/Getty Images; R32(TC) ©Image Source, (TR) Lori Adamski-Peek/Jupiter Images, (BR) Jupiter Images; R34 (BR) Getty Images; R35 (TR) Jupiter Images; R36 (TL) Getty Images, (CL) ©Purestock/Alamy, (C) Jupiter Images, (CL) ©Jupiterimages/Creatas/Alamy; R37 (CR) ©Image Source; R38 (TL) Blend Images/Jupiter Images, (TC) Rolf Bruderer/Corbis, (TR) Stephen Weistead/Corbis, (BL) ©Jupiterimages/BananaStock/Alamy; R39 (TL) Getty Images, (TC) Corbis/Jupiter Images; R41 (TR) ©DK/Getty Images.